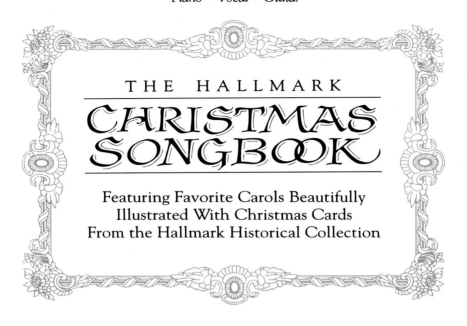

THE HALLMARK
CHRISTMAS SONGBOOK

Featuring Favorite Carols Beautifully
Illustrated With Christmas Cards
From the Hallmark Historical Collection

From the Hallmark Historical Collection. This is a reproduction of an early twentieth century postcard designed by Ellen Clapsaddle, and originally printed in Germany for the International Art Publishing Company.

Previously published as part of
The Christmas Card Songbook

Hal Leonard Publishing Corporation
7777 West Bluemound Road
P.O. Box 13819   Milwaukee, WI 53213

Published by HAL LEONARD PUBLISHING CORPORATION
P.O. Box 13819, 7777 W. Bluemound Rd.
Milwaukee, WI 53213 USA

Printed in China

CONTENTS

8   **The Story Of The Christmas Card**

11   **The Symbols Of Christmas As Reflected On Christmas Cards**

16   **A History Of The Christmas Carol**

19   Angels We Have Heard On High

25   Away In A Manger (Murray)

29   Away In A Manger (Spilman)

33   Deck The Hall

37   First Noel, The

41   From Heaven Above To Earth I Come

43   Go, Tell It On The Mountain

47   God Rest Ye Merry, Gentlemen

51   Hark! The Herald Angels Sing

55   Holly And The Ivy, The

59   It Came Upon The Midnight Clear

63   Jingle Bells

67   Jolly Old St. Nicholas

71   Joy To The World

75   Mary Had A Baby

79   O Christmas Tree

83   O Come, All Ye Faithful

87   O Come, O Come Emmanuel

91   O Holy Night

97   O Little Town Of Bethlehem

101   Rise Up, Shepherd, And Follow

105   Silent Night

109   Twelve Days Of Christmas, The

113   Up On The Housetop

117   We Three Kings Of Orient Are

121   We Wish You A Merry Christmas

125   What Child Is This?

PREFACE

Christmas carols and cards are two of the most cherished traditions associated with the world's favorite holiday. Over the centuries, hundreds of artists and composers have been inspired by the Yuletide season, creating classics in art and music that live on year after year. It seems only natural that these two elements should be combined in THE HALLMARK CHRISTMAS SONGBOOK.

We at Hallmark Cards are pleased to offer THE HALLMARK CHRISTMAS SONGBOOK featuring designs from the Hallmark Historical Collection, one of the most significant collections of cards in the world. As you enjoy these beloved Christmas songs and the timeless designs which have helped people share the spirit of this special season through the years, may you and those you love experience the full meaning of Christmas...the beauty and joy of its traditions, the reassurance of its message of hope and peace, and the gift of love that caring people everywhere can share.

THE STORY OF THE CHRISTMAS CARD

The joy of sending and receiving Christmas cards has a colorful history dating to the days of the stagecoach and penny postage.

More than a century ago, in 1843, London businessman Henry Cole originated the Christmas card custom. His idea of Christmas in an envelope came only three years after the English postal reform that made it possible to send mail to friends near and far for a penny.

Cole asked an artist friend, John Calcott Horsley of the Royal Academy, to design the card in 1843, when Cole didn't have time to write the customary personal messages. The card was divided into three panels, with the main illustration showing the elders at a friendly family party raising glasses in a toast. The panels on either side showed two of the oldest traditions of Christmas – feeding the hungry and clothing the needy. "A Merry Christmas and A Happy New Year To You," still the most popular holiday sentiment, was the message.

Original prints of the card are both rare and valuable. Only a dozen are known to exist, including two in the Hallmark Historical Collection, one of the most significant collections of cards in the world. The collection contains over 100,000 printed artifacts from the 19th and 20th centuries, including Hallmark product.

Greeting card firms began springing up in England during the 1860s. England's best known woman artist and illustrator of children's books, Kate Greenaway, designed greeting cards for Marcus Ward and Co. of London.

Popular Christmas card designs of the 1860s and '70s included few religious scenes. The most popular designs were landscapes, children, flowers, portraits, birds, animals and fish.

Louis Prang of Boston perfected in the 1870s the lithographic process of multicolor printing, often using as many as 20 colors on one card. His reproductions of oil paintings were so accurate that at times only experts could tell print from painting.

Hallmark Product Archives, Hallmark Cards, Inc.

8

By 1881, Prang was printing 5 million cards a year, most of them Christmas cards. He sponsored art contests to get card designs, with prizes as high as $1,000.

Near the turn of the century, penny postcards made in Germany flooded the market. Rather than compromise the quality of his cards, Prang discontinued their manufacture in 1895. From then until World War I, Germany monopolized the postcard trade.

At this time, most of today's major greeting card publishers began to emerge, including Hallmark Cards, in 1910. By 1920, the new card companies were meeting the public demand for cards of better quality and design.

In 1929, the Depression hit. Cards of the period often spoofed poverty and expressed faith that better times were ahead.

The industry survived the Depression only to run head-on into World War II. Santa and Uncle Sam carrying flags became popular designs. Special cards came out for servicemen. "Across The Miles" and "Missing You" sentiments reflected the reality of the day.

The Cold War years sharpened a demand for more humor in Christmas cards. This sparked the studio card, with its funny Santas and silly reindeer.

Hallmark Product Archives, Hallmark Cards, Inc.

THOUGH YOU WON'T GET HOME THIS SEASON, STILL THERE ISN'T ANY REASON YOU CAN'T HAVE A "MERRY CHRISTMAS" WHILE IN CAMP, FOR ALL SOLDIER BOYS ARE BROTHERS AND JUST DOING THINGS FOR OTHERS IS A WAY TO KEEP YOUR SPIRITS FAR FROM DAMP.

NOW FOR CHRISTMAS CELEBRATIONS YOU MUST MAKE SOME PREPARATIONS AND THERE'LL BE SOME SPECIAL THINGS YOU'LL NEED, OF COURSE,

Hallmark Product Archives, Hallmark Cards, Inc.

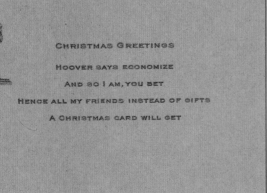

CHRISTMAS GREETINGS
HOOVER SAYS ECONOMIZE
AND SO I AM, YOU BET
HENCE ALL MY FRIENDS INSTEAD OF GIFTS
A CHRISTMAS CARD WILL GET

Hallmark Product Archives, Hallmark Cards, Inc.

Flower children, peace symbols and designs celebrating the first manned moon landing came into vogue during the 1960s and '70s. In the early 1980s, cards depicted the fitness craze, showing Santa outfitted in jogging suit and running shoes, and participating in sports. Other cards captured the '80s by spoofing TV shows and commercials.

Today's trends in Christmas cards show a renewed interest in traditional designs (trees, wreaths, red and green, home settings) that are both colorful and elegant. Religious cards remain popular, and many of them are contemporary, using bright graphics with short, upbeat prose sentiments.

The Christmas card-sending custom has weathered war, economic turmoil and vast social changes for more than a century. It serves a timeless human need to stay close, to share special thoughts and feelings with friends far and near during our most cherished holiday season.

Each year it is estimated that 2.2 billion Christmas cards will be given.

THE SYMBOLS OF CHRISTMAS AS REFLECTED ON CHRISTMAS CARDS

Christmas cards aren't always what they appear to be.

Ever since the first-known commercially printed Christmas greeting was designed in 1843 in London, critics have complained about the lack of attention to the religious aspect of the holiday. Very often the religious symbolism is there, but unrecognized by the layman.

Even the first card, which was criticized by temperance groups because it pictured a family with wine glasses raised in a toast, was full of symbolism. Artist John Calcott Horsley, who designed the card for London businessman Henry Cole, made good use of the religious symbolism of Christmas. His side panels depicted the virtues of feeding the poor and clothing the naked. But more than that, Horsley wound sprigs of holly, the symbol of chastity, and ivy, symbolic of where God had walked, through the design.

In the Hallmark Historical Collection, one of the most representative collections of early greeting card art in the world, one can see such design elements as evergreens, birds, animals and musical instruments used to symbolize the rich traditions and legends of Christmas.

One of the most popular images used by the early designers was the robin. According to legend, a small brown bird fanned the embers of a dying fire in the manger one night to keep the Christ Child warm. As the flames leapt from the coals, the little bird's breast was seared scarlet, but he kept at his chore. Today, artists use the robin red breast to symbolize courage and charity.

© Hallmark Cards, Inc.

11

CHRISTMAS.

Let us be joyful on this joyful day!
With grateful memories let us praise and pray
On Christmas Day!

And while our friends at home are glad and gay,
Let us remember those who are far away
On Christmas Day!

Let them in fancy hear us as we say
"Health be with thee, and plenty guide thy way
On Christmas Day"!

Accept this record of the debt we pay,
A debt of Love to thee on Christmas Day,
On Christmas Day!

Flying birds frequently symbolize spiritual life and a peacock in a design stands for eternal life. And, of course, the dove traditionally has been the sign of peace.

Lambs symbolize Christ, who was the Lamb of God, and call attention to His later sacrifice on the cross, while sheep are used to indicate that all living things owe allegiance to their Creator. Such beasts of burden as oxen and donkeys often symbolize humility.

Many of the legends from which artists have borrowed ideas revolve around trees and flowers.

The white rose that appears on many Christmas cards comes from the tale of the little shepherd girl who broke into tears as she walked to the manger because she had no gift for the Christ Child. An angel, seeing her plight, turned her tears into white roses with which to decorate the manger.

CHRISTMAS SCATTER MANY JOYS ABOUT YOU!

The poinsettia had a similar beginning. In a Mexican folk tale, a peasant boy who had no money for a gift gathered simple greenery along the road to Bethlehem. But before he arrived at the manger, an angel appeared and turned the green leaves to scarlet flowers.

Nothing plays a more symbolic part in the art of Christmas than the evergreen, which is the subject of many legends.

According to one, on the night Christ was born, all the trees in the forest burst into bloom in honor of the birth, and have continued to bear fruit year round ever since.

The legend of the pine tree tells us that the pine was once mortal. Like other trees, it was green in summer, bare and brown in winter.

One giant pine tree, its branches brittle and half its trunk hollowed out by disease, stood by a road in Israel where Joseph and Mary passed as they fled with the Christ Child from the soldiers of King Herod. Joseph led Mary and the Child into the hollow trunk to rest and hide. The pine tree, full of pity, dropped its protective branches down to cover them while Herod's troops rode by. All night it hid them. The next morning, the Child awoke and blessed the pine tree and pronounced that forevermore its branches would be green both summer and winter.

The Germans have provided us with one of the more delightful folk tales about the origin of the Christmas tree. According to the legend, just as a woodsman and his family were about to retire on Christmas Eve, there was a knock on the door. It was a small child, shivering with cold and hunger. The family took the child in, fed him, and gave him a place to sleep.

The next morning the family was awakened by a choir of angels caroling in the sky. To their joy and amazement, they discovered that it was the Christ Child whom they had entertained. He stood before them transfigured, and before he disappeared, he took a twig from a fir tree, planted it in the ground and said: "I have gladly received your gifts, and here is mine to you; this tree will never fail to bear its fruit at Christmas and you shall always have abundance."

The use of an evergreen as a Christmas tree comes to us from Germany, and while Christmas trees are believed to have been introduced into this country by Hessian soldiers during the Revolutionary War, the custom came into its own only about 100 years ago.

Symbolic significance of the evergreen branches of the Christmas tree is tied closely to the Christian belief in everlasting life.

Martin Luther is frequently credited with originating the custom of decorating evergreen trees and bringing them into the house. And the decorations have their legends and symbolism, too.

The Glory of God is symbolized by Christmas lights and the red holly berries commonly used for decoration in earlier years symbolize the drops of blood caused by the crown of thorns.

The use of tinsel on Christmas trees springs from an old story about some little house spiders who spun their silk to decorate the bare tree of a poor but good German woman who had been kind to them. An angel, impressed by their charity, touched the tree and turned the spider webs to shining silver.

Mistletoe was first used by the British along with holly and ivy to decorate their somber halls. Since mistletoe was a key part of ancient Druid winter solstice rites, church authorities in England banned the bush from churches for a time. The custom of kissing under the mistletoe springs, by the way, from the Druid tradition of marrying under giant oak trees decorated with mistletoe.

13

From the Hallmark Historical Collection. Reproduced from an original 19th century card published by Obpacher Brothers, Munich.

From the Hallmark Historical Collection. From an original early 20th century postcard.

From the Hallmark Historical Collection. This is a reproduction of an early 20th century postcard design published by Philip Sander in 1906.

No story about Christmas cards would be complete without Santa Claus. And artists have portrayed Santa in a variety of ways.

Until Dr. Clement Clarke Moore wrote his classic poem, "A Visit from St. Nicholas," in 1822, and described Santa Claus as a right jolly old elf with a white beard and a little round belly, there was no accepted way that Santa was supposed to look.

Even then, it took another forty years before political cartoonist Thomas Nast, the man who created the elephant and donkey symbols for the two major political parties, popularized Moore's Santa in his drawings for magazines and newspapers.

Until that time, Santa took on whatever form the artist imagined.

Some Santas were thin and in some cases bore striking resemblance to popular leaders.

The most popular Santa of the old days, however, was the Father Christmas figure, a stately, bearded gentleman dressed in clerical robes.

Hallmark's research has revealed that "Santa Claus" is a distortion of "Saint Nicholas," who was brought to this country in the early 18th century by Dutch colonists. Saint Nicholas was difficult for children to pronounce, so the name was simplified in stages: first to "sinterklas," and finally to "Santa Claus."

The original Saint Nicholas is believed to have been a 4th century archbishop of Myra, a city in Turkey, who devoted his life to good deeds and gift-giving.

For many years in Europe, the gift-giving that we associate with Christmas took place on December 6, St. Nicholas Day, and even today in many Catholic countries, children receive gifts from St. Nicholas on December 6.

When the Protestant Reformation swept over Northern Europe, the reformers attempted to wipe out all veneration of saints. One of the targets was Saint Nicholas.

But the Protestants, or perhaps the children of the Protestants, borrowed a chapter from their Catholic predecessors. As the Catholics had "Christianized" certain pagan festivals, so did the Protestants "Protestantize" certain Catholic festivals.

As a result, Saint Nicholas began to pop up all over Europe at Christmas with a different name: Père Noël in France, Father Christmas in England, Kris Kringle in Germany.

Whatever he was called, and whenever he came, Santa Claus brought gifts to children. He loved them. And they loved him.

In Europe, Santa Claus traveled by popular conveyance – in many cases, horsedrawn cart.

The sleigh with its reindeer is a purely American invention with the first known reference appearing in 1821 in a publication called "The Children's Friend."

But it took time, even in America, for Santa to move exclusively to the sleigh. Some early greeting cards in the Hallmark Historical Collection show him arriving by other means. One shows Santa riding an antique bicycle.

Even though the facts point to the American Santa Claus being of Dutch origin, greeting cards as we know them today are a phenomenon of the English-speaking world. As a result, the Father Christmas figure was more often used on antique Christmas cards.

But Thomas Nast changed that when his drawings began appearing in the 1860s, and by the time that the modern era of greeting card publishing began, approximately 1910, Santa Claus as we know him today was firmly established.

Christmas cards have come a long way since 1843. Designs are more sophisticated. Production processes have been refined. But the message on that first Christmas card is as relevant today as it was then.

"A Merry Christmas and a Happy New Year to You."

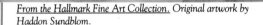

From the Hallmark Fine Art Collection. Original artwork by Haddon Sundblom.

From the Hallmark Historical Collection. Reproduced from an original 1886 card published by Louis Prang, Boston; designed by Walter Satterlee.

Hallmark Product Archives, Hallmark Cards, Inc.

HISTORY OF THE CHRISTMAS CAROL

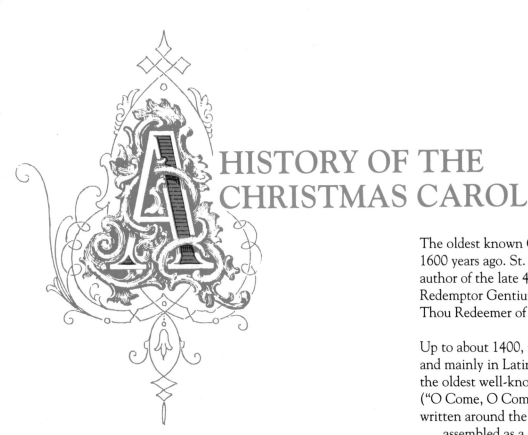

The oldest known Christmas song was written about 1600 years ago. St. Ambrose of Italy was probably the author of the late 4th century Latin carol, "Veni, Redemptor Gentium." In its English form, "Come, Thou Redeemer of the Earth," it is still sung today.

Up to about 1400, relatively few carols were created, and mainly in Latin and Greek. The components of the oldest well-known carol, "Veni, Emmanuel" ("O Come, O Come, Emmanuel") were probably written around the 12th century. However, it was not assembled as a carol until the mid-nineteenth century. If "O Come, O Come, Emmanuel" is not to be regarded as the earliest famous carol, then that honor would go to "La marche des rois" ("The March Of The Kings"), a vigorous 13th century folk phenomenon from Provence, France.

Around 1400 in England, and somewhat earlier on the continent, two changes developed in the carol. First, vernacular or national languages steadily replaced Latin and Greek. Second, the carol evolved as a popular dance form. This new type of song was a reaction to the strictness and puritanism of the Middle Ages and the increased secularism and humanism of the blossoming Renaissance. The carol really began to flourish in the 15th century, producing enduring songs like "The Boar's Head Carol" and "Coventry Carol," both from England, and "Es ist ein' Ros' Entsprungen" ("Lo, How a Rose E'er Blooming") from Germany.

Hallmark Product Archives, Hallmark Cards, Inc.

The 16th century was the greatest era for the carol. That fertile period probably produced "God Rest Ye Merry, Gentlemen," "The First Noel," "We Wish You A Merry Christmas," and the dominant tune for "What Child Is This?" in England, "Deck The Hall" in Wales, and "O Tannenbaum" ("O Christmas Tree") and "Von Himmel hoch, da komm Ich her" ("From Heaven Above To Earth I Come") in Germany.

16

But in the 17th and 18th centuries, the carol suffered a decline. In fact, the secular celebration of Christmas was actually banned in England for a few years starting in 1644. Yet several fine carols were created in this lesser period. England was once again the land of carols, producing the folk songs "The Holly And The Ivy" and "The Twelve Days Of Christmas," plus the lyrics for "Joy To The World" and "Hark! The Herald Angels Sing." In addition, "Adeste Fideles" ("O Come All Ye Faithful") was created in France.

The carol bounced back strongly in the 19th century with a serious interest in collecting and printing old carols, plus the composition of a number of new songs. In Austria, the most popular carol, "Stille Nacht, Heilige Nacht" ("Silent Night, Holy Night") was written. In France, "Cantique Noël" ("O Holy Night") was composed. In England, the lyrics for "What Child Is This?" were created. In Germany, the tune for "Hark! The Herald Angels Sing" was composed.

Carol creation was actively pursued in the United States at the same time, primarily after mid-century. The music for "Joy To The World" and the lyrics for "It Came Upon the Midnight Clear," "We Three Kings Of Orient Are," "Jingle Bells," "O Little Town of Bethlehem," "Jolly Old St. Nicholas," and "Go, Tell It On The Mountain" made the 19th century in America an exceptional era.

Numerous Christmas songs were conceived in the 20th century, but religious carols were few, especially after World War II. Building on the artistic promise of the late 19th century, the United States clearly became the leader. The most productive period was the 1930s, 1940s and 1950s, which brought us many popular favorites.

Since the 1950s, few good Christmas songs have been written. Perhaps the 1990s and the 21st century will bring a revival of carol production, including some significant religious tributes to the holidays.

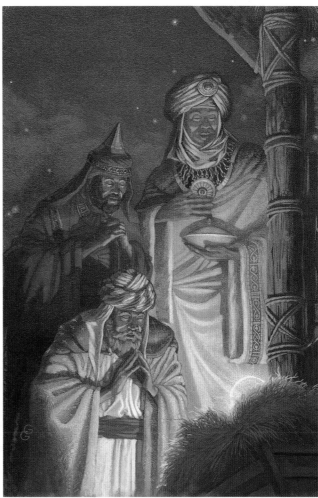

From The Hallmark Historical Collection. This is a reproduction of a card from the Artistic Series published by Raphael Tuck & Sons, London, ca. 1883.

ANGELS WE HAVE HEARD ON HIGH

Historical confusion muddles the background of this splendid carol and its most common English translation. Despite wild claims of second century origins and similar misinformation, the anonymous song is almost surely from 18th century France. The translation first appeared in England in 1862, but did not take its familiar form until a 1916 American carol collection.

18

ANGELS WE HAVE HEARD ON HIGH

French-English

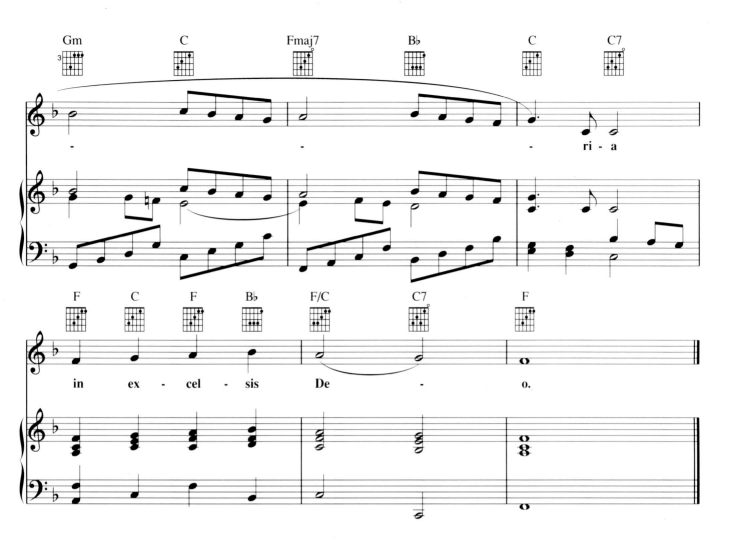

- - ri - a

in ex - cel - sis De - o.

23

AWAY IN A MANGER (Murray)

No matter what you may have heard, Martin Luther was in no way associated with "Away In A Manger." The words were anonymous, and were first published in Philadelphia in 1885. The first (and most popular) melody connected with the lyrics was composed by American James Ramsey Murray in 1887. The "Carl Mueller" sometimes mentioned as composer of the tune appears to be totally imaginary.

AWAY IN A MANGER

Music by
JAMES R. MURRAY

WAY IN A MANGER (Spilman)

There have been many variant melodies connected with this carol's anonymous words, which were first published in Philadelphia in 1885. The second most popular tune is the march-like setting written by American Jonathan E. Spilman in 1838. Spilman's melody was originally intended for the English folk ballad "Flow Gently Sweet Afton."

AWAY IN A MANGER

Music by
JONATHAN E. SPILMAN

ECK THE HALL

If any carol could be characterized as totally uninhibited, it would be
this very merry tribute to holiday pleasure. The historical background
on the song is fuzzy, but it appears that the compelling lyrics (originally
probably in English) and the exceptional melody are both from Wales.
The best guess as to dating it would be the 16th century.

DECK THE HALL

Welsh

From the Hallmark Historical Collection. Reproduced from an original 1910 postcard
published by International Art Publishing Co., Germany. Designed by Ellen Clapsaddle.

THE FIRST NOEL

In spite of the common use of the word "Noel" with this folk carol, the song is not French in origin, but is instead completely English. More properly called "The First Nowell," it is a product of 16th century Cornwall, a remote southwestern region of England. Although the lyrics are not particularly good, the enduring melody makes the carol among the most popular pieces from Britain.

THE FIRST NOEL

Additional Lyrics

2. They looked up and saw a star
   Shining in the East, beyond them far;
   And to the earth it gave great light,
   And so it continued both day and night.

3. And by the light of that same star,
   Three wise men came from country far;
   To seek for a King was their intent,
   And to follow the star wherever it went.

4. This star drew night to the northwest,
   O'er Bethlehem it took its rest;
   And there it did both stop and stay,
   Right over the place where Jesus lay.

5. Then entered in those wise men three,
   Full reverently upon their knee;
   And offered there in His presence,
   Their gold, and myrrh, and frankincense.

FROM HEAVEN ABOVE TO EARTH I COME

Martin Luther reportedly wrote the 1535 lyrics as part of a Christmas Eve ceremony for his son Hans. Four years later, he composed the famous melody. Of entirely German Christmas songs, only "O Christmas Tree" is better known. This great chorale, adapted by Bach for his 1734 "Christmas Oratorio," has been dubbed "the carol of the Reformation."

FROM HEAVEN ABOVE TO EARTH I COME

MARTIN LUTHER, 1539
Translated by CATHERINE WINKWORTH, 1855
Harmonized by J.S. BACH, 1734

O, TELL IT ON THE MOUNTAIN

This exuberant Black spiritual, created late in the 19th century or very
early in the 20th century, is one of the very finest carols ever conceived. It
is probably anonymous, but may possibly have been the work of Frederick
J. Work, a Black Nashville-born composer.

GO, TELL IT ON THE MOUNTAIN

Black Spiritual,
ca. 1900

CHRISTMAS.

Let holly deck the rafters and mistletoe beside,
For token of the holy time, for joy of Christmas-tide.

From the Hallmark Historical Collection.

GOD REST YE MERRY, GENTLEMEN

In Charles Dickens' 1843 Christmas classic, Scrooge chased away
a young London caroler who was singing "God Rest Ye Merry,
Gentlemen." Therefore, this song is the Christmas carol of "A
Christmas Carol." From the 16th century, it quite possibly originated
with the Waits of London, a city supported band. Despite the word
"merry" in the title and the lively, exotic melody, this superb
composition is a religious piece.

GOD REST YE MERRY, GENTLEMEN

English Folk Carol,
16th century

A MERRY CHRISTMAS & A HAPPY NEW YEAR

From the Hallmark Historical Collection. Reproduced from an original 19th century card
published by Joseph Mansell, London.

HARK! THE HERALD ANGELS SING

Two giants produced this great carol. Englishman Charles Wesley, co-founder of Methodism and perhaps the top hymn writer in the English language, wrote the words in 1739. Note how the verses are saturated with theology. Almost every line is a sermon. German classical master Felix Mendelssohn composed the melody for an 1840 choral work. Different from most carols, the tune is actually a military style march!

HARK! THE HERALD ANGELS SING

Words by CHARLES WESLEY, 1739
Music by FELIX MENDELSSOHN, 1840

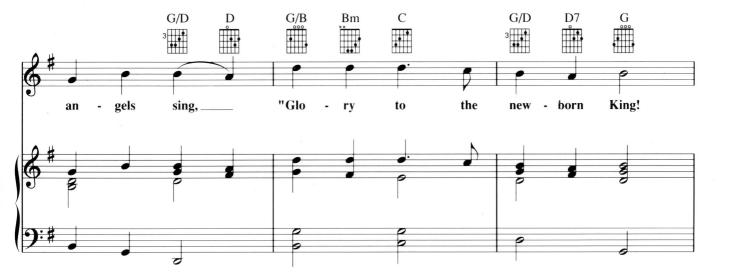

Peace on earth, and mer - cy mild, _____ God and sin - ners re - con - ciled." Joy - ful all ye na - tions rise, _____ Join the tri - umph of the skies; _____ With th' an - gel - ic host pro - claim, "Christ is _____ born in

Beth - le - hem." Hark! The her - ald an - gels sing,

"Glo - ry _____ to the new - born King!"

From the Hallmark Historical Collection. This is a reproduction of a design by Emily J. Harding, originally published in c.1880 by Raphael Tuck and Sons of London.

THE HOLLY AND THE IVY

Accompanying one of the most attractive and buoyant of carol melodies is perhaps the least understood set of carol lyrics. The holly and the ivy are medieval symbols of the rivalry between the sexes, with the holly representing males and the ivy females. This celestial folk mini-masterpiece was conjured up in England around 1700.

THE HOLLY AND THE IVY

English Folk Carol, ca. 1700

Additional Lyrics

2. The holly bears a blossom,
   As white as lily flow'r,
   And Mary bore sweet Jesus Christ,
   To be our Saviour.

3. The holly bears a berry,
   As red as any blood,
   And Mary bore sweet Jesus Christ,
   To do poor sinners good.

 IT CAME UPON THE MIDNIGHT CLEAR

Massachusetts minister Edmund Hamilton Sears created this classic poem of optimism in a wintry setting in December 1849. Boston born journalist and musician Richard Storrs Willis composed the excellent, flowing melody in 1850. Soon after, some unknown person (perhaps Willis) combined verses and melody to synthesize the first world class American carol.

58

IT CAME UPON THE MIDNIGHT CLEAR

Words by EDMUND H. SEARS, 1849
Music by RICHARD S. WILLIS, 1850

heav'n's ____ all - gra - cious King." ____

____ The world in sol - emn

still - ness lay, To hear the

an - gels sing. _____

From the Hallmark Historical Collection. This is a reproduction of a postcard printed in Germany, c.1914.
Postcards were a popular form of greeting during that era and were often collected and preserved in albums.

JINGLE BELLS

When Boston-born James S. Pierpont devised this little ditty for a
Sunday school class in 1857, he surely had no idea he was creating
America's first outstanding secular Christmas song and probably its
most popular. Incidentally, "Jingle Bell Rock," the best Christmas
rock song, was written by Joseph Beal and James Boothe exactly one
hundred years later, in 1957.

JINGLE BELLS

Words and Music by
J. PIERPONT

JOLLY OLD ST. NICHOLAS

This bright and lively American holiday favorite, quite popular among children, is anonymous. It was probably written in the second half of the 19th century or very early in the 20th. There is a chance it was composed by Benjamin R. Hanby, who created the similar style "Up On The Housetop" in the 1850's or 1860's.

JOLLY OLD ST. NICHOLAS

Jol - ly old Saint Nich - o - las,
When the clock is strik - ing twelve,

lean your ear this way.
when I'm fast a - sleep,

Don't you tell a
Down the chim - ney

sin - gle soul
broad and black,

what I'm going to say,
with your pack you'll

say.
creep.

68

From the Hallmark Historical Collection. *Reproduced from an original 19th century card published by Charles Goodall & Son, London.*

JOY TO THE WORLD

The verses for this spectacular carol were penned in 1719 by Englishman Isaac Watts, whose English language hymn writing accomplishments are only challenged by Charles Wesley. In 1839, the lyrics were published with a sweeping, dynamic melody accompanied by a notation attributing the music to German master George Frederick Handel. But the real composer of the tune was American hymnist Lowell Mason who first published it.

JOY TO THE WORLD

ISAAC WATTS, 1719,
LOWELL MASON, 1839

71

MARY HAD A BABY

The fragile image of the blessed young woman Mary with her helpless
infant Christ child was a popular theme in Black-American carols.
This piece, among the best of its type, was probably created in the
19th century, possibly in South Carolina.

MARY HAD A BABY

Black Spiritual
probably 19th century

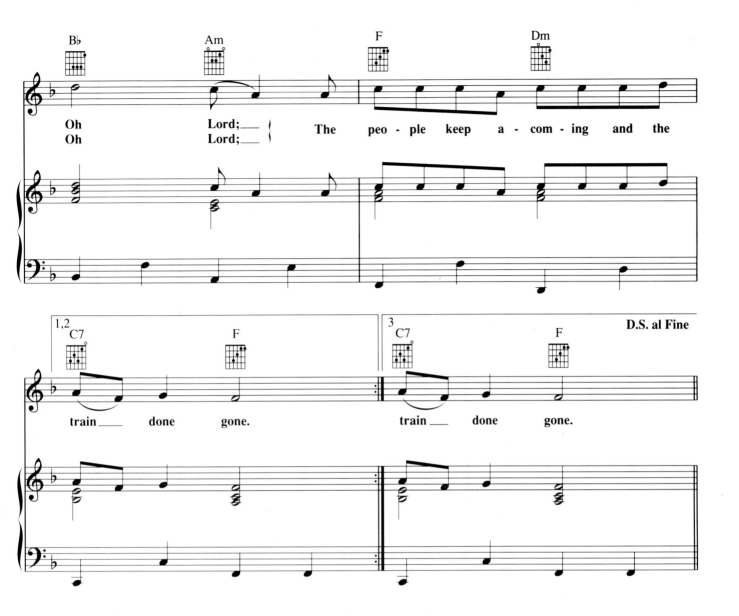

Additional Lyrics

5. Born in a stable, Oh Lord;
   Born in a stable, Oh my Lord;
   Born in a stable, Oh Lord;
   The people keep a-coming and the train done gone.

6. Where did they lay Him? Oh Lord;
   Where did they lay Him? Oh my Lord;
   Where did they lay Him? Oh Lord;
   The people keep a-coming and the train done gone.

7. Laid Him in a manger, Oh Lord;
   Laid Him in a manger, Oh my Lord;
   Laid Him in a manger, Oh Lord;
   The people keep a-coming and the train done gone.

 CHRISTMAS TREE

It has sometimes been thought that this German folk carol originated in the Middle Ages. Yet the style of the music plus the fact that Christmas trees were not a popular holiday institution until the 16th century suggest that the song was created around the 16th or 17th centuries. The melody is excellent, but the German words and all English translations seem awkward.

O CHRISTMAS TREE

German

O Christ - mas tree! O Christ - mas tree, you
Christ - mas tree! O Christ - mas tree, much
Christ - mas tree! O Christ - mas tree, thy

stand in ver - dant beau - ty! O Christ - mas tree! O
pleas - ure doth thou bring me! O Christ - mas tree! O
can - dles shine out bright - ly! O Christ - mas tree! O

 COME, ALL YE FAITHFUL

Catholic Englishman John Francis Wade, a music teacher and
music copyist, wrote this magnificent Latin carol between 1740
and 1743 while living in Douai, France. For two centuries, English,
German, Italian, and Portuguese origins were claimed. Because of
this background and the song's great world-wide acceptance, it
deserves the epithet of "the international carol."

O COME, ALL YE FAITHFUL

JOHN FRANCIS WADE, between 1740 and 1743;
Translated by FREDERICH OAKELEY, 1852

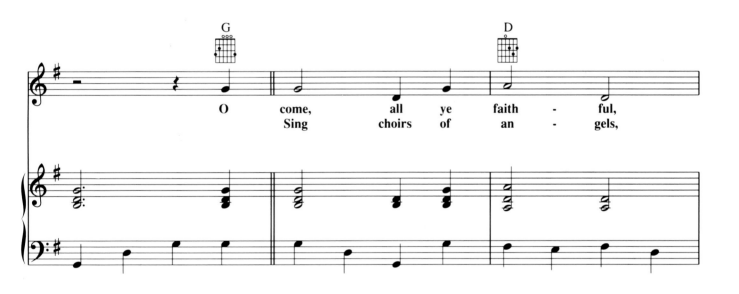

O come, all ye faith - ful,
Sing choirs of an - gels,

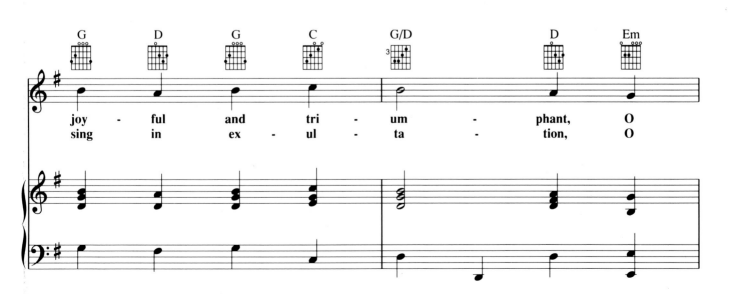

joy - ful and tri - um - phant, O
sing in ex - ul - ta - tion, O

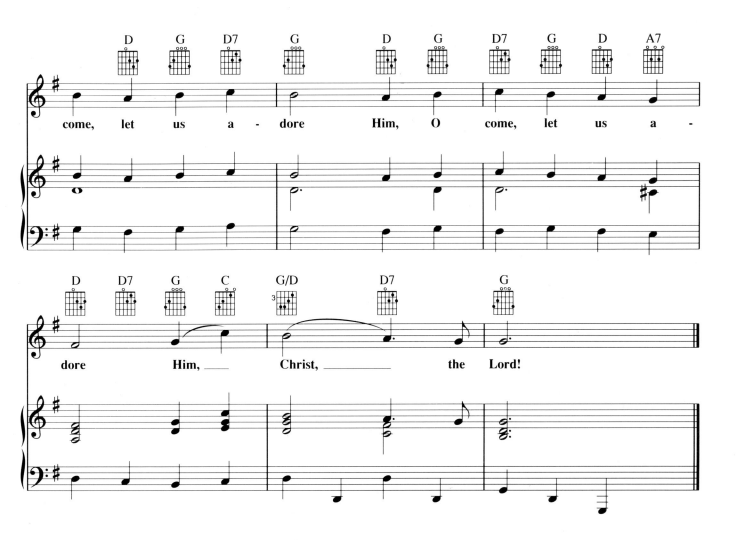

come, let us a - dore Him, O come, let us a - dore Him, _____ Christ, _____ the Lord!

 COME, O COME EMMANUEL

This soulful Advent carol could be called "a carol of two centuries."
Both its original Latin lyrics and its melody (supposedly a plainsong
or chant) are said, without proof, to be from about the 12th century.
But it was not assembled as a carol until 1854 when two Englishmen,
Thomas Helmore and John Mason Neale, published it. Reportedly,
Helmore adapted the old music and Neale translated the words (with
later modifications by Henry S. Coffin).

O COME, O COME EMMANUEL

Translated by JOHN M. NEALE
and HENRY S. COFFIN
Possibly 12th century

From the Hallmark Historical Collection. Reproduced from an original 19th century card published by Marcus Ward & Co., London.

HOLY NIGHT

In December 1847, Placide Cappeau, a commissionaire of wines and part-time poet from southern France, travelled to Paris to visit the celebrated classical composer Adolphe Adam. The musician consented to write a melody to go with Cappeau's just completed Christmas poem. The resultant carol, the greatest Christmas song from France, premiered that year at Cappeau's home church.

O HOLY NIGHT

English Words by J.S. DWIGHT
Music by ADOLPHE ADAM

94

LITTLE TOWN OF BETHLEHEM

In December 1868, Philadelphia clergyman Phillips Brooks penned
some verses reminiscing on a trip to the Holy Land a few years earlier.
His friend Lewis H. Redner, a real estate broker and part-time organist,
was asked to supply a musical setting for an upcoming Sunday school
program. Redner reportedly went to bed the night before the program
and woke up with "an angel strain" sounding in his head. He jotted
down some notes and a classic was born.

O LITTLE TOWN OF BETHLEHEM

Words by PHILLIPS BROOKS, 1868
Music by LEWIS H. REDNER, 1868

light;   The   hopes   and   fears   of
birth!   And   prais - es   sing   to

all   the   years   Are   met   in   thee   to - night.
God   the   King,   And   met   peace   to   men   on   earth!

RISE UP, SHEPHERD, AND FOLLOW

Published in 1867, this excellent Black spiritual probably dates from the late 18th or early 19th century. Frequently, a solo voice sings the verses followed by a vocal ensemble responding with the key phrase, "Rise up, shepherd, and follow."

RISE UP, SHEPHERD, AND FOLLOW

Black Spiritual

ILENT NIGHT

Except for a series of accidents, the greatest of carols would not have
been created. Because the organ at the church in Oberndorf, Austria
had become unplayable because of rust in 1818, Father Joseph Mohr
wrote a simple set of lyrics and organist Franz Grüber created a simple
melody to use in the Christmas Eve service. Mohr, a problem priest
who was frequently transferred, was not at Oberndorf long. And
Gruber was supposed to be at another church. Furthermore, the song
would have died there if it were not for the organ repairman who
obtained a copy and began its spread around the world.

SILENT NIGHT

Words by JOSEPH MOHR
Music by FRANZ GRÜBER

heav - en - ly   peace.
Sav - ior is   born!
Lord at Thy   birth.

From the Hallmark Historical Collection. Reproduced from an original 19th century card
published by Marcus Ward & Co., London.

© *Hallmark Cards, Inc.*

THE TWELVE DAYS OF CHRISTMAS

With an accessible melody and clever counting lyrics, this 17th or 18th century English folk phenomenon is always a big hit at Christmas. It's a song conducive to tinkering and variation, and a song with a most charming personality. The concept for the composition may have come from France, where a similar piece exists.

THE TWELVE DAYS OF CHRISTMAS

English Folk Song,
17th or 18th century

UP ON THE HOUSETOP

Little known Ohioan Benjamin R. Hanby wrote this children's favorite sometime in the 1850s or 1860s. It is possible that Hanby also created "Jolly Old St. Nicholas," an anonymous holiday song with similar style lyrics and music.

UP ON THE HOUSETOP

By BENJAMIN R. HANBY

Down thru the chim - ney with good Saint Nick.

© Hallmark Cards, Inc.

 E THREE KINGS OF ORIENT ARE

This pseudo-oriental classic, with a compelling melody and somewhat clumsy lyrics has often been regarded as an old song. But it was created in 1857, the same year that the newer-sounding "Jingle Bells" came to life. Its author was Pittsburgh-born clergyman, journalist, and artist John Henry Hopkins who offered it to his Vermont nephews and nieces as a Christmas gift.

WE THREE KINGS OF ORIENT ARE

Words and Music by
JOHN H. HOPKINS, 1857

Westward leading, still proceeding,
Guide us to thy perfect light.

WE WISH YOU A MERRY CHRISTMAS

Although not the most brilliantly conceived composition ever, this jolly and attracting folk concoction very pleasantly continues to spread holiday greetings century after century. It was created in the West Country of England, quite possibly in the highly productive 16th century.

WE WISH YOU A MERRY CHRISTMAS

English

Brightly

mf

We wish you a Mer-ry Christ-mas, We

wish you a Mer-ry Christ-mas, We wish you a Mer-ry

Christ-mas, and a hap-py New Year. Good

WHAT CHILD IS THIS?

The lyrics by English insurance executive and occasional poet
William Chatterton Dix, written around 1865, are quite good. But it
is the exquisite English folk melody, also known as "Greensleeves,"
which makes this carol exceptional. "Greensleeves," which has been
wrongly attributed to King Henry VIII, was most likely created during
the second half of the 16th century (about the time of Shakespeare
and Queen Elizabeth I).

WHAT CHILD IS THIS?

English

greet _____ with an - thems sweet _____ While
kings _____ sal - va - tion brings, _____ Let

shep - herds watch _____ are keep -
lov - ing hearts _____ en - throne

ing? This,
Him. Raise,

this _____ is
raise _____ the

Christ the King, _____ Whom shep - herds
song on high, _____ The Vir - gin

PEACE